LUDOVICO EINAUDI

for guitar

arrangements by
Giovanni Bailo

This book is printed on FSC paper.
The FSC logo identifies products which contain paper from well managed forests
certified in accordance with the rules of Forest Stewardship Council.

Thanks to Warner Chappell Music Italiana s.r.l.

Special thanks to Davide Mastrangelo.

CD tracks recorded by Giovanni Bailo
Giovanni Bailo plays Coriani and Ragghianti Guitars
contact: giovanni.bailo@fastwebnet.it

BELLA NOTTE

Music by Ludovico Einaudi

TRACK 1

Arranged by Giovanni Bailo

Minuetto

Andante scorrevole

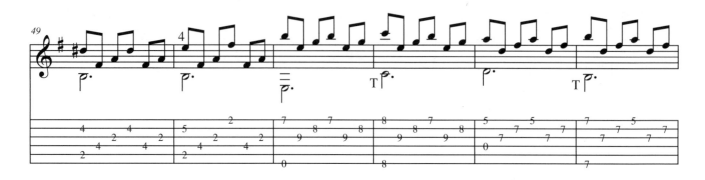

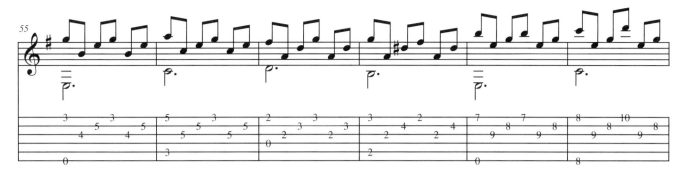

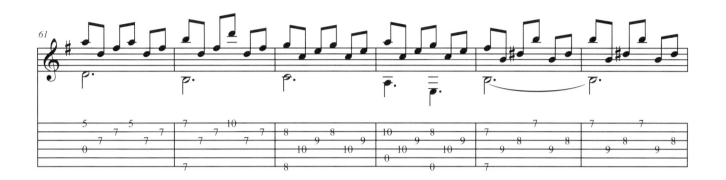

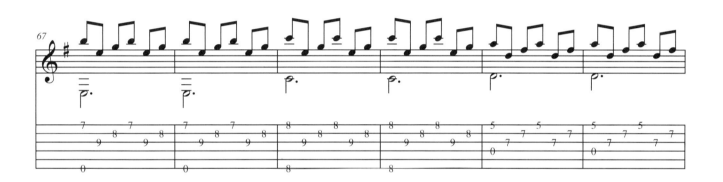

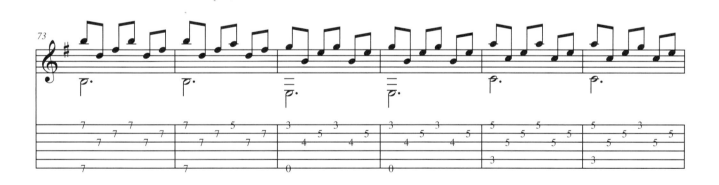

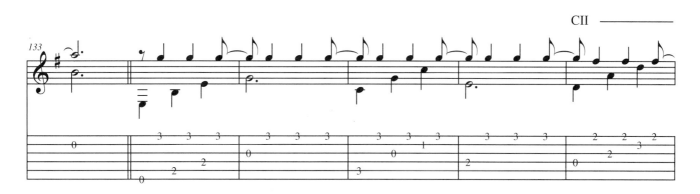

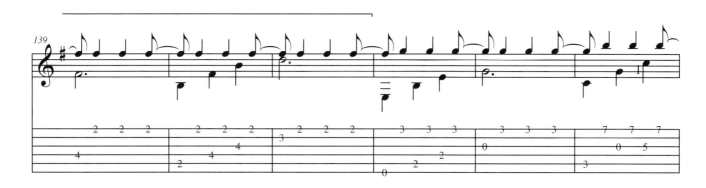

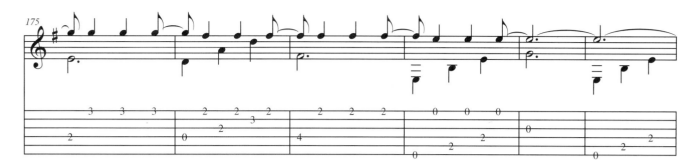

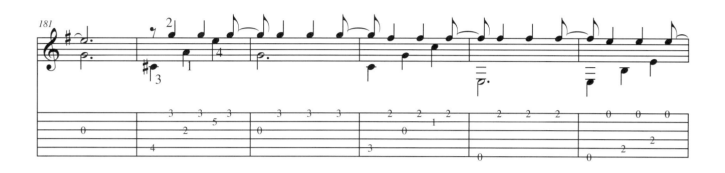

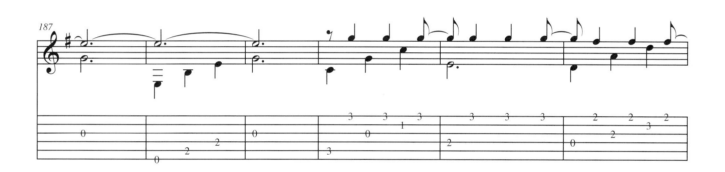

GIORNI DISPARI

Music by Ludovico Einaudi

Arranged by Giovanni Bailo

Partial Capo on 6th string, first fret (see Note)

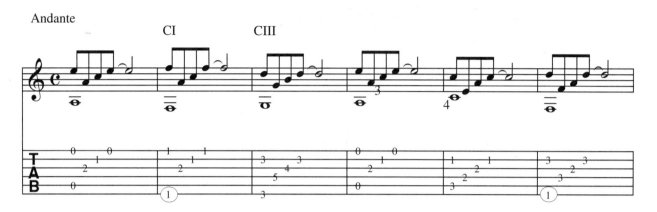

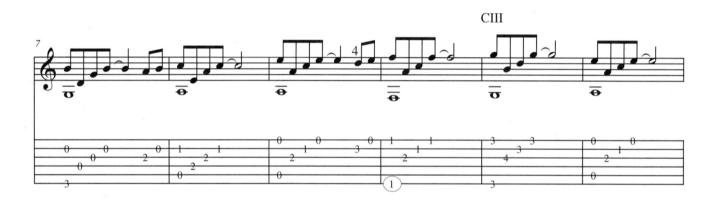

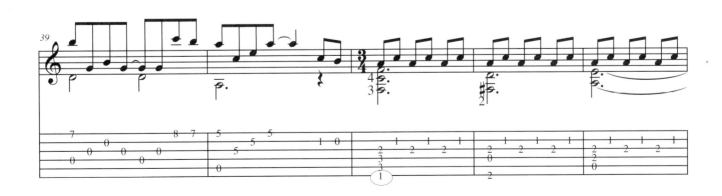

Note: *number "1" inside the circle on the sixth string in tablature, is equivalent of "0" due to the partial capo*

I DUE FIUMI

Music by Ludovico Einaudi

Arranged by Giovanni Bailo

Andante con moto

15

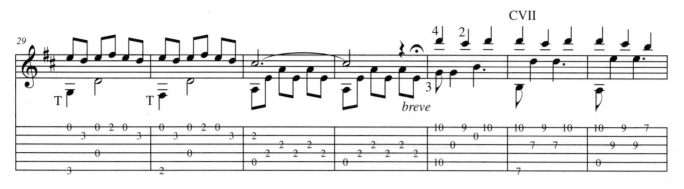

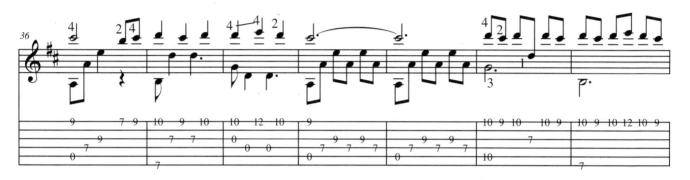

CII

Coda

JULIA

Music by Ludovico Einaudi

Arranged by Giovanni Bailo

Andante scorrevole

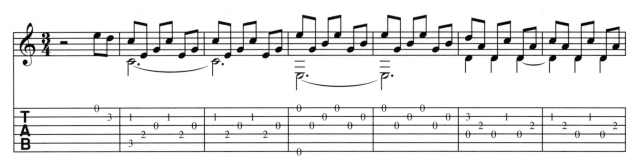

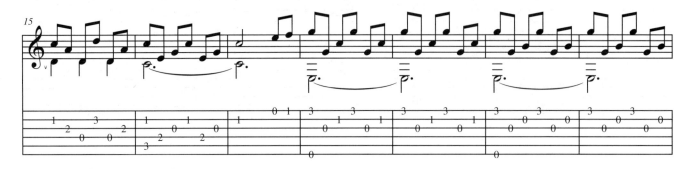

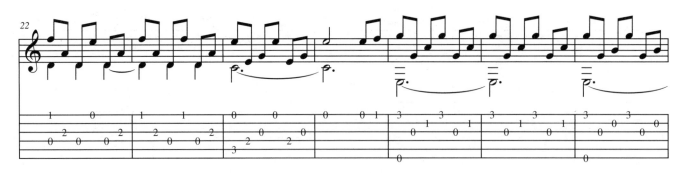

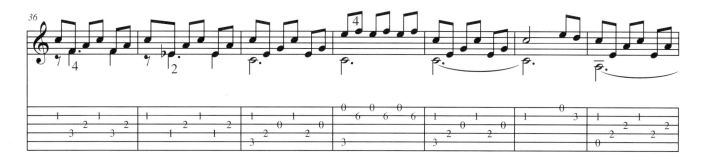

CI

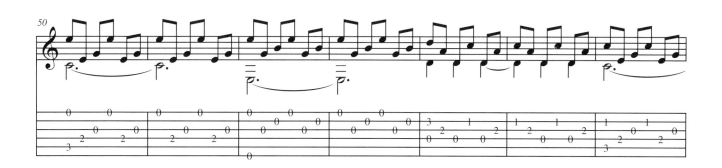

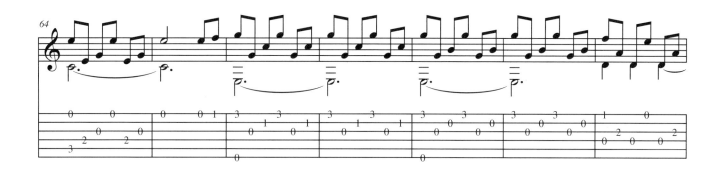

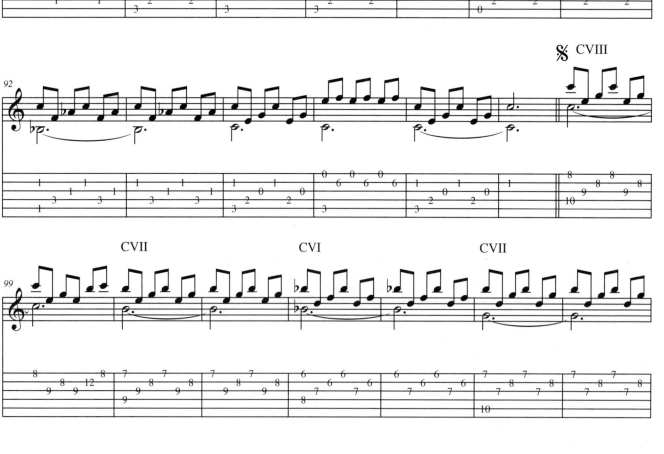

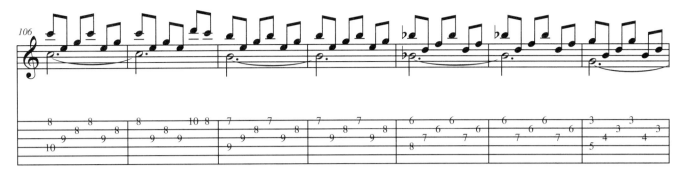

CI

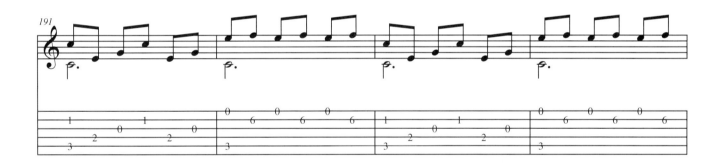

Allargando

NEFELI

Music by Ludovico Einaudi

Arranged by Giovanni Bailo

Partial Capo on 6th string, first fret (see Note)
Andante con moto

Note: *number "1" inside the circle on the sixth string in tablature, is equivalent of "0" due to the partial capo*

PASSWORD

Music by Ludovico Einaudi

Arranged by Giovanni Bailo

Adagio, come un carillon

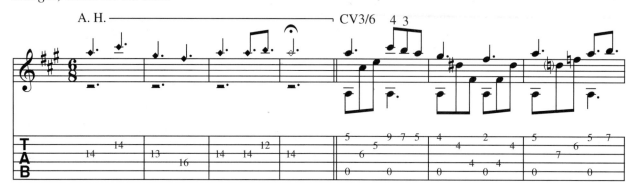

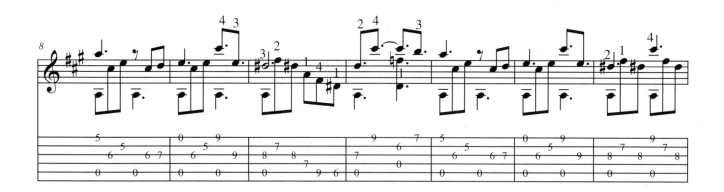

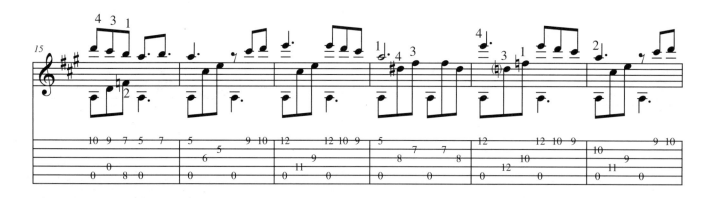

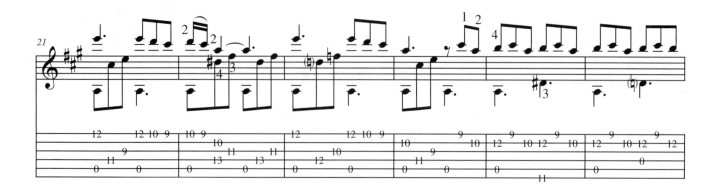

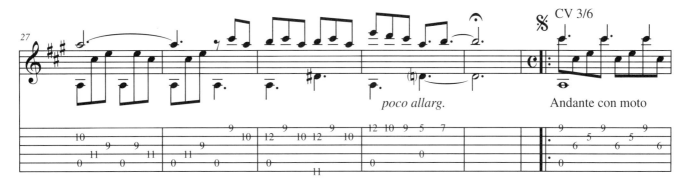

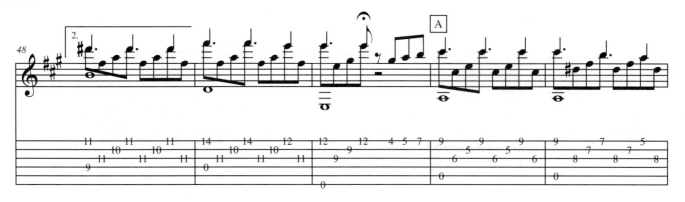

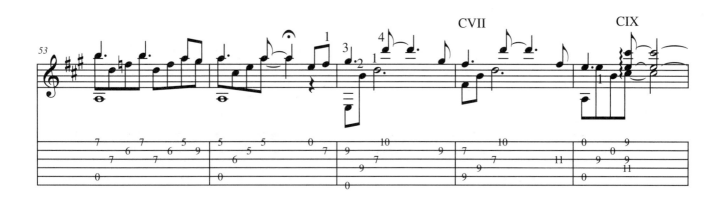

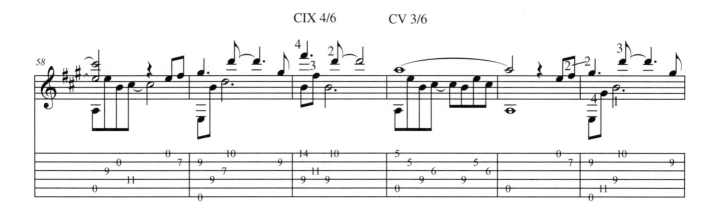

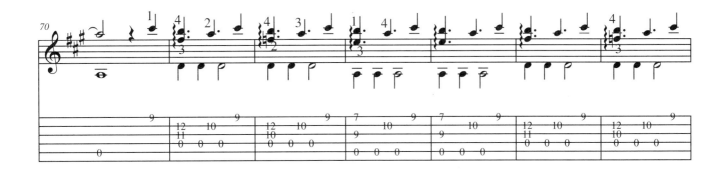

STELLA DEL MATTINO

Music by Ludovico Einaudi

Arranged by Giovanni Bailo

Capo II

Andante con moto

LE ONDE

Music by Ludovico Einaudi

TRACK 8

Arranged by Giovanni Bailo

dolce e cantabile, marcando la melodia

MB206

MB175

MB76

MB132

MB70

MB152

MB87

MB139

MB78

MB89

MB138

MB102

MB182